EASIEST KEYBOARD COLLECTION

Love Songs

WISE PUBLICATIONS
London/New York/Paris/Sydney/Copenhagen/Madrid

Exclusive Distributors:

Music Sales Limited
8/9 Frith Street,
London W1V 5TZ, England.

Music Sales Pty Limited
120 Rothschild Avenue,
Rosebery, NSW 2018,
Australia.

Order No. AM950708
ISBN 0-7119-7048-3
This book © Copyright 1998 by Wise Publications

Book design by Chloë Alexander
Compiled by Peter Evans
Music arranged by Derek Jones
Music processed by Paul Ewers Music Design

Printed in the United Kingdom by
Caligraving Limited, Thetford, Norfolk.

Photographs courtesy of:
Image Bank

Your Guarantee of Quality
As publishers, we strive to produce every book to the highest
commercial standards.
The music has been freshly engraved and the book has been carefully
designed to minimise awkward page turns and to make playing from
it a real pleasure.
Particular care has been given to specifying acid-free, neutral-sized
paper made from pulps which have not been elemental chlorine
bleached. This pulp is from farmed sustainable forests and was
produced with special regard for the environment.
Throughout, the printing and binding have been planned to ensure
a sturdy, attractive publication which should give years of enjoyment.
If your copy fails to meet our high standards, please inform us and
we will gladly replace it.

Music Sales' complete catalogue describes thousands of titles and is
available in full colour sections by subject, direct from Music Sales
Limited. Please state your areas of interest and send a cheque/postal
order for £1.50 for postage to: Music Sales Limited, Newmarket Road,
Bury St. Edmunds, Suffolk IP33 3YB.

Contents

A TIME FOR US
(Love Theme From Romeo & Juliet)

Music By Nino Rota
Words by Eddie Snyder & Larry Kusic

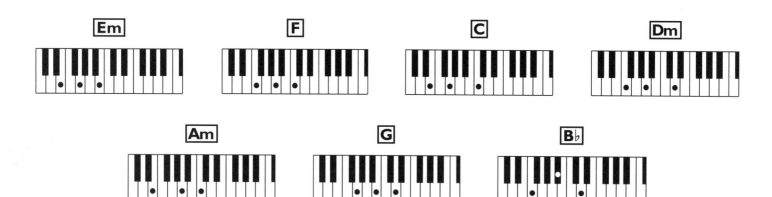

Voice: **Choir**

Rhythm: **Samba**

Tempo: ♩ = 104

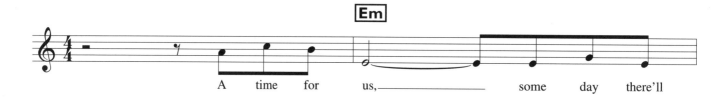

A time for us,———— some day there'll

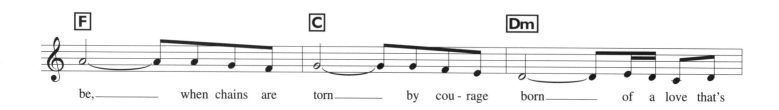

be,———— when chains are torn——— by cou - rage born——— of a love that's

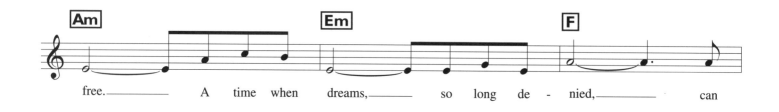

free.———— A time when dreams,——— so long de - nied,———— can

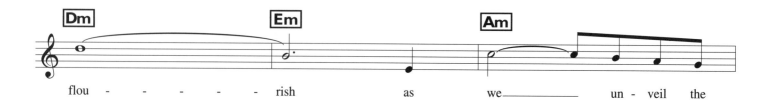

flou - - - - rish as we——— un - veil the

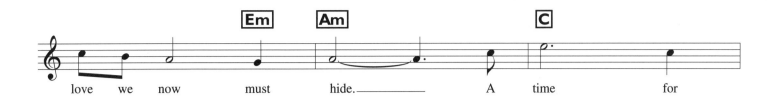

love we now must hide._____ A time for

us_____ at last to see,_____ a

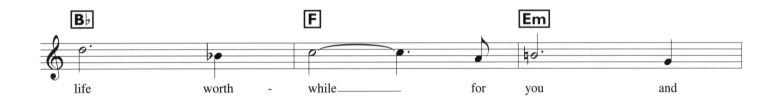

life worth - while_____ for you and

me._____ And with our love,_____ through tears and thorns,_____ we will en -

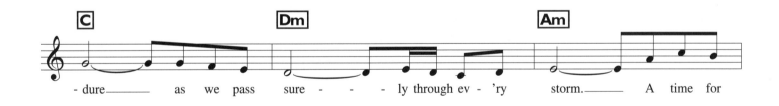

- dure_____ as we pass sure - - ly through ev - 'ry storm._____ A time for

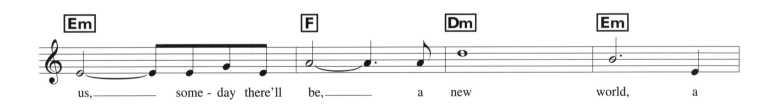

us,_____ some - day there'll be,_____ a new world, a

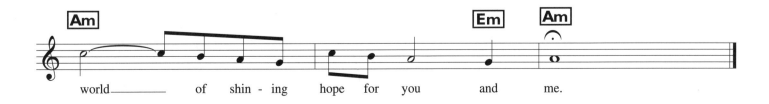

world_____ of shin - ing hope for you and me.

ALL THE WAY

Words by Sammy Cahn
Music by James Van Heusen
© Copyright 1957 Maraville Music Corporation, USA.
The International Music Network Limited,
Independent House, 54 Larkshall Road Chingford, London E4 6PD.

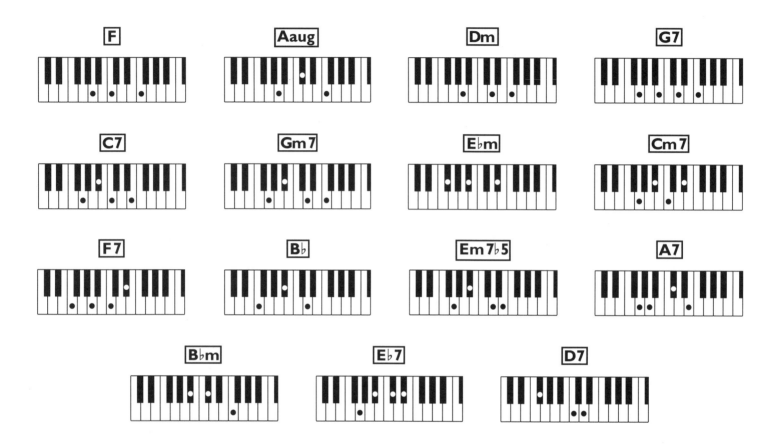

Voice: **Clarinet**

Rhythm: **16 Beat**

Tempo: ♩ **= 76**

When some-bo-dy loves you, it's no good un-less he loves you (she) all the

way. Hap-py to be near you, when you need some-one to cheer you

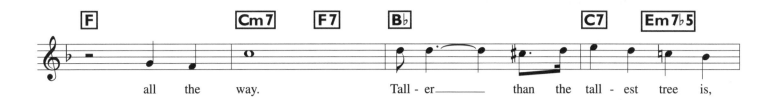

all the way. Tall - er_____ than the tall - est tree is,

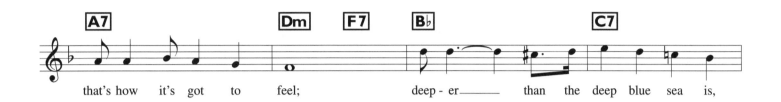

that's how it's got to feel; deep - er_____ than the deep blue sea is,

that's how deep it goes_ if it's real. When some-bo-dy needs you, it's no good un-less he needs you (she)

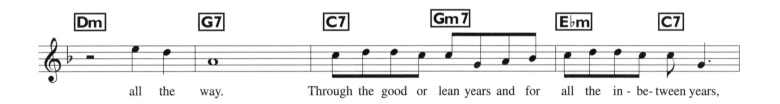

all the way. Through the good or lean years and for all the in - be-tween years,

come what may. Who knows_____ where the road will lead us?

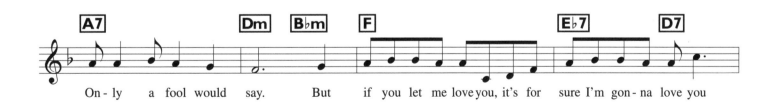

On - ly a fool would say. But if you let me love you, it's for sure I'm gon - na love you

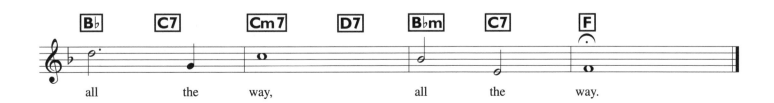

all the way, all the way.

COME LIVE YOUR LIFE WITH ME

Words & Music by Nino Rota, Billy Meshel & Larry Kusic
© Copyright 1970 Famous Music Corporation, USA.
All Rights Reserved. International Copyright Secured.

Voice: **Saxophone**

Rhythm: **Jazz Waltz**

Tempo: ♩ = 132

No - one can buy to - mor - row,

no - one can sell their sor - row.

But when you look in - to my eyes,

darl - ing you'll al - ways see

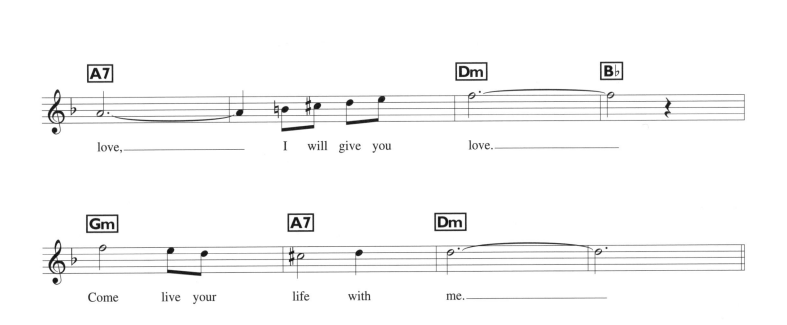

love,_____ I will give you love._____

Come live your life with me._____

No - one can buy to - mor - row,_____

no - one can sell their sor - row._____ But when you

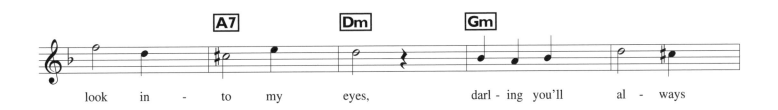

look in - to my eyes, darl - ing you'll al - ways

see_____ love,_____ I will give you love._____

_____ Come live your life with me._____

DREAM LOVER

Words by Clifford Grey
Music by Victor Schertzinger
© Copyright 1929 Famous Music Corporation, USA.
Cambell Connelly & Company Limited, 8/9 Frith Street, London W1.
All Rights Reserved. International Copyright Secured.

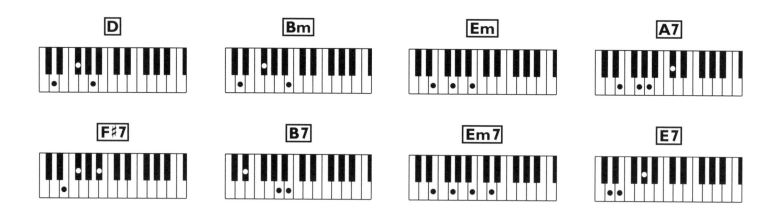

Voice: **Jazz Organ**

Rhythm: **Jazz Waltz**

Tempo: ♩ = 92

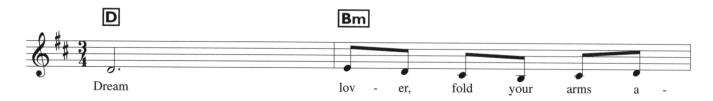

Dream   lov - er,   fold   your   arms   a -

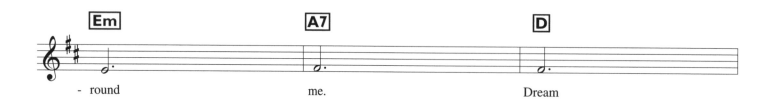

- round   me.   Dream

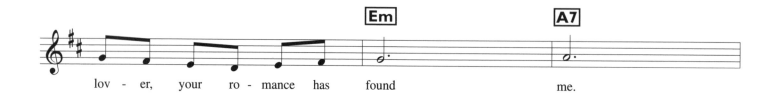

lov - er,   your   ro - mance   has   found   me.

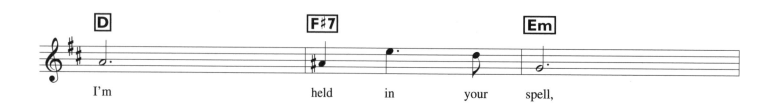

I'm   held   in   your   spell,

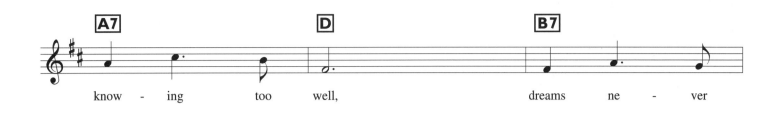

know - ing too well, dreams ne - ver

tell._____ We

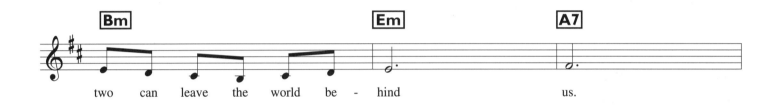

two can leave the world be - hind us.

No - - - bo - dy in - dis - creet can find

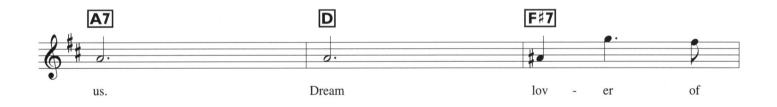

us. Dream lov - er of

mine, sec - rets di - vine, I am

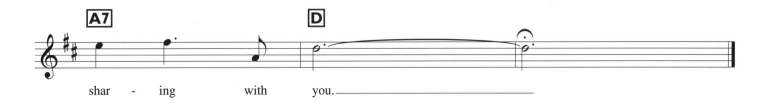

shar - ing with you._____

FALLING IN LOVE AGAIN

Music & Original Words by Freidrich Hollander
English Words by Reg Connelly

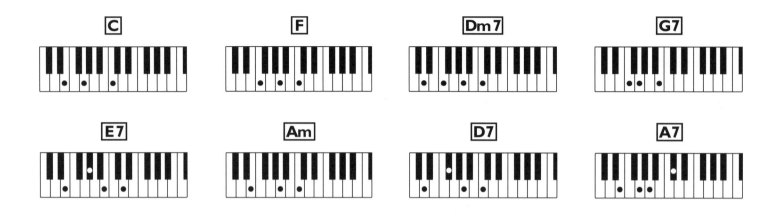

Voice: **Saxophone**

Rhythm: **Jazz Waltz**

Tempo: ♩ = 108

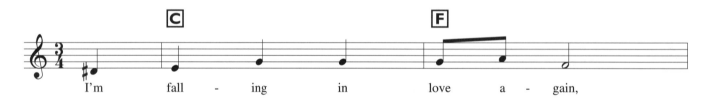

I'm fall - ing in love a - gain,

ne - ver want - ed to, what am I to

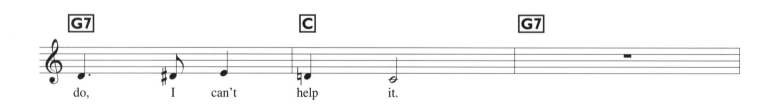

do, I can't help it.

Love's al - ways been my game play it how I

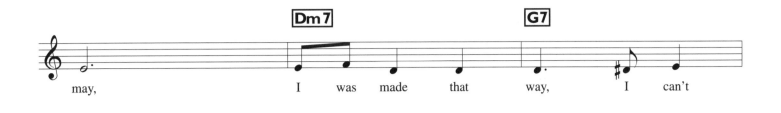

may, I was made that way, I can't

help it. Men clus - ter

to me like moths a - round a flame,

and if their wings burn I know I'm not to

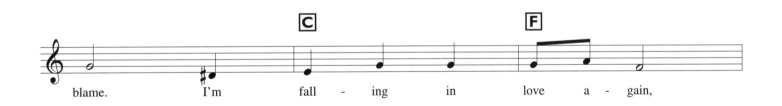

blame. I'm fall - ing in love a - gain,

ne - ver want - ed to, what am I to

do, I can't help it.

I'LL REMEMBER APRIL

Words & Music by Don Raye, Gene de Paul & Patricia Johnson

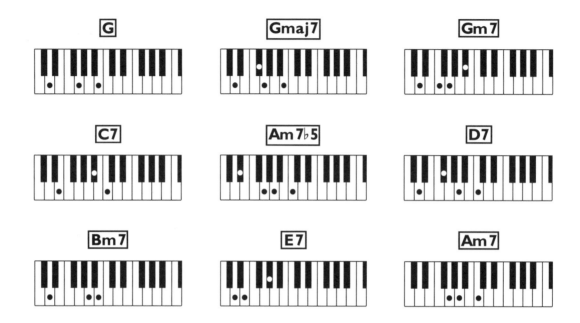

Voice: **Strings**

Rhythm: **Ballad**

Tempo: ♩ = 126

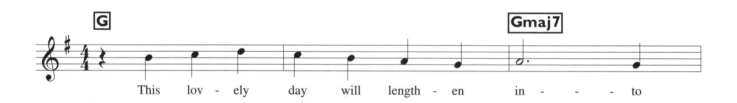

This lov - ely day will length - en in - - to

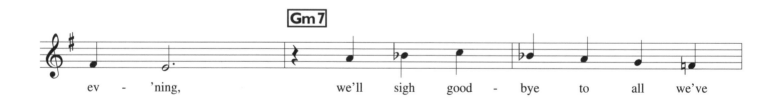

ev - 'ning, we'll sigh good - bye to all we've

ev - er had._____ A - lone, where

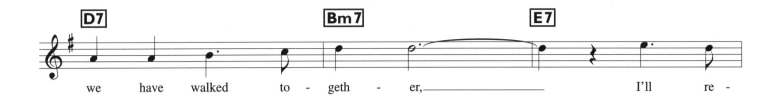

we have walked to - geth - er,_____ I'll re -

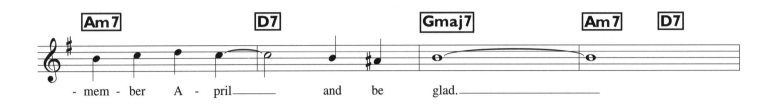

- mem - ber A - pril_____ and be glad._____

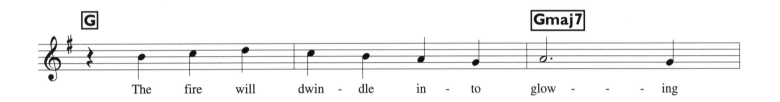

The fire will dwin - dle in - to glow - - - ing

ash - es, for flames and love live such a

lit - tle while._____ I won't for - get,_____

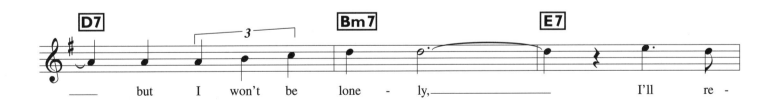

_____ but I won't be lone - ly,_____ I'll re -

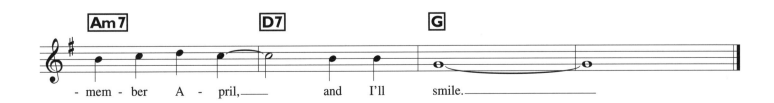

- mem - ber A - pril,_____ and I'll smile._____

IT COULD HAPPEN TO YOU

Music by Jimmy Van Heusen
Words by Johnny Burke

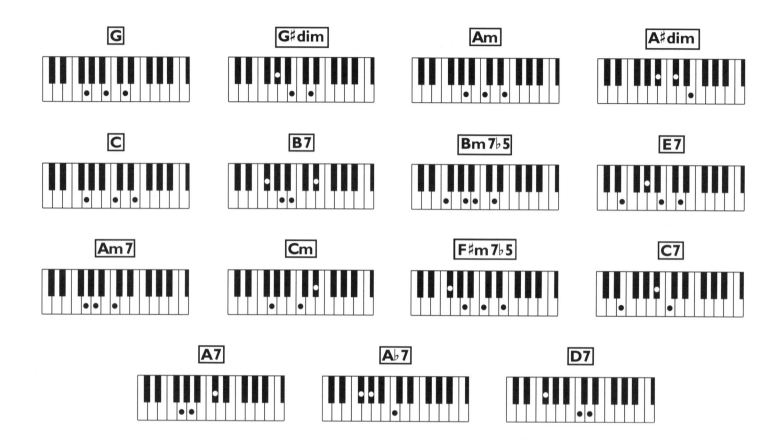

Voice: **Jazz Organ**

Rhythm: **Ballad**

Tempo: ♩ = 98

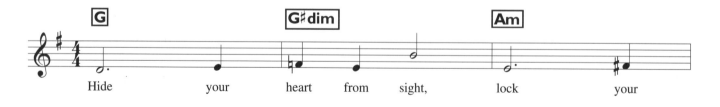

Hide   your   heart   from   sight,   lock   your

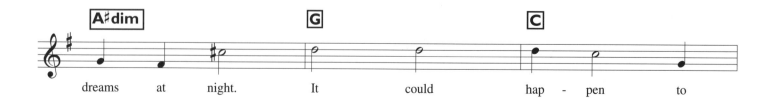

dreams   at   night.   It   could   hap - pen   to

you.___ Don't count stars or you might

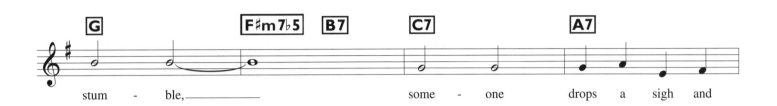

stum - ble,___ some - one drops a sigh and

down you tum - ble. Keep an eye on Spring,

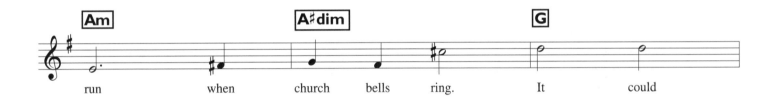

run when church bells ring. It could

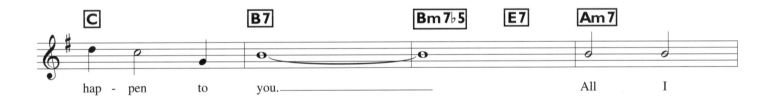

hap - pen to you.___ All I

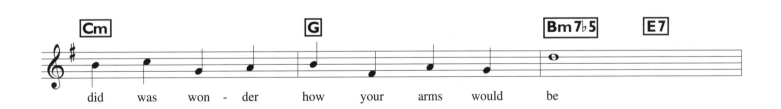

did was won - der how your arms would be

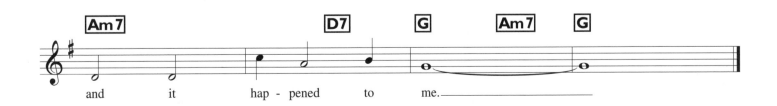

and it hap - pened to me.___

JUST THE TWO OF US

Words & Music by Ralph MacDonald, William Salter & Bill Withers

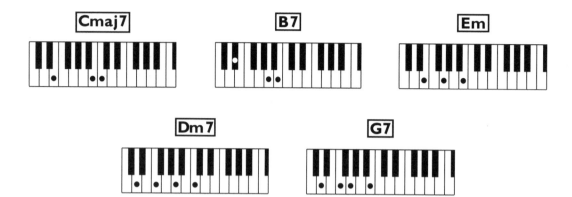

Voice: **Jazz Organ**

Rhythm: **16 Beat**

Tempo: ♩ **= 80**

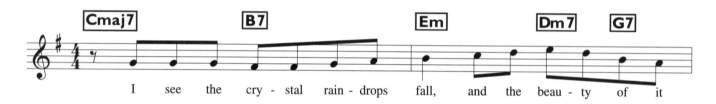

I see the cry - stal rain - drops fall, and the beau - ty of it

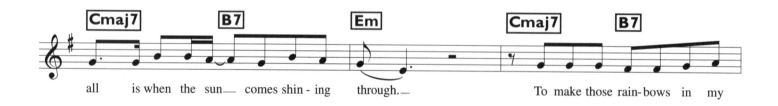

all is when the sun— comes shin - ing through.— To make those rain - bows in my

mind, when I think of you some time, and I want to spend— some time with you.— Just the

two of us,— we can make it if— we try,— just the two of us.— (Just the

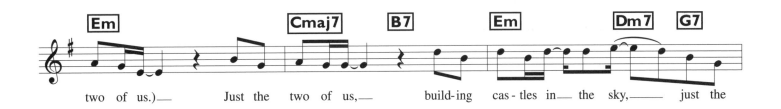

two of us.)— Just the two of us,— build-ing cas-tles in— the sky,— just the

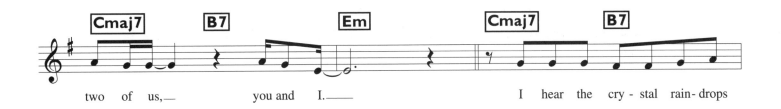

two of us,— you and I.— I hear the cry-stal rain-drops

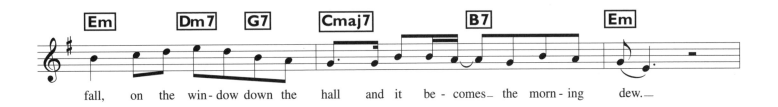

fall, on the win-dow down the hall and it be-comes— the morn-ing dew.—

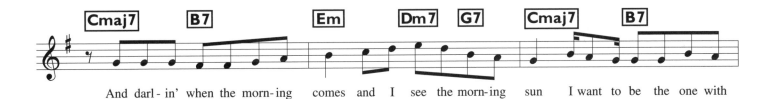

And darl-in' when the morn-ing comes and I see the morn-ing sun I want to be the one with

you.— Just the two of us,— we can make it if— we try,— just the

two of us.— (Just the two of us.)— Just the two of us,— build-ing

cas-tles in— the sky,— just the two of us,— you and I.—

LET'S PUT IT ALL TOGETHER

Words & Music by Hugo Perreti, Luigi Creatore & George David Weiss

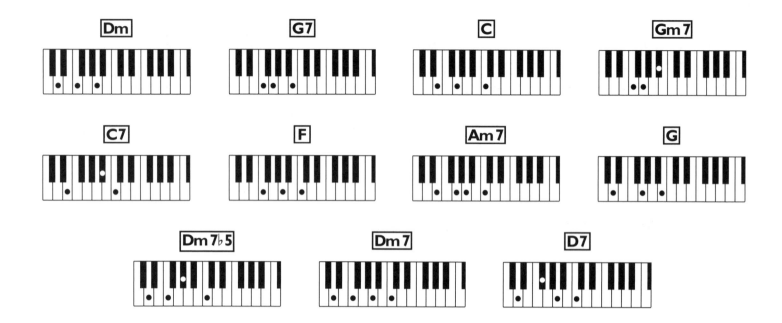

Voice: **Saxophone**

Rhythm: **Ballad**

Tempo: ♩ = 88

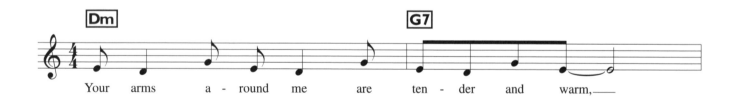

Your arms a - round me are ten - der and warm,

my arms____ are meant to hold you.____ Your arms and my arms,

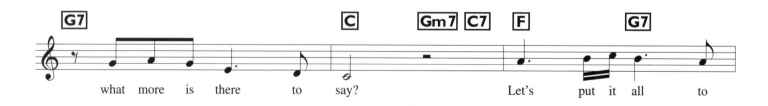

what more is there to say? Let's put it all to

- ge - ther,_____ let's put it all to - geth - er._____ Let's put it all to -

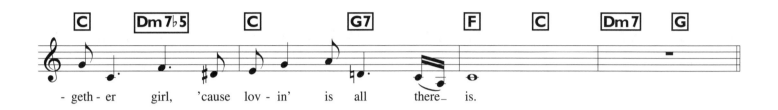

- geth - er girl, 'cause lov - in' is all there__ is.

Love like this ne - ver hap - pened be - fore,__ per - fect_____ and

true. Day by day we been feel - in' it more,__ you love me_____ and

I love you. Let's put it all to - geth - er,_____

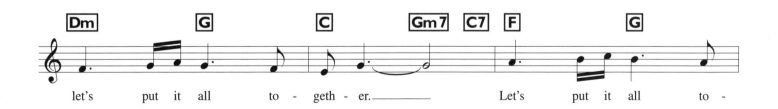

let's put it all to - geth - er._____ Let's put it all to -

Repeat to fade

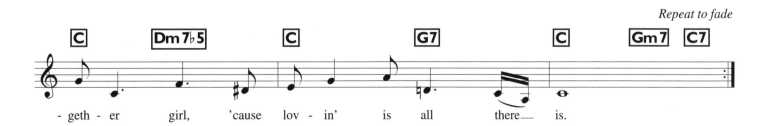

- geth - er girl, 'cause lov - in' is all there__ is.

LOVE ME WITH ALL YOUR HEART
(Cuando Calienta El Sol)

Music by Carlos Rigual & Carlos A. Martinoli
Original Words by Mario Rigual
English Lyric by Michael Vaughn

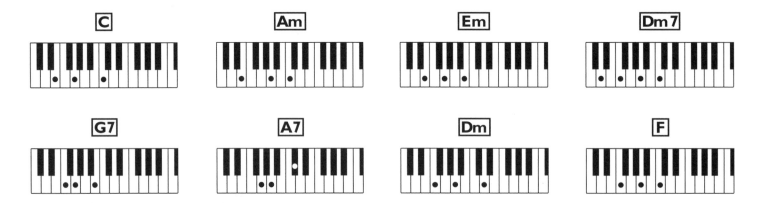

Voice: Accordion
Rhythm: Slow Rock (12/8)
Tempo: ♩. = 80

Love me with all your heart,— that's all I want love.—

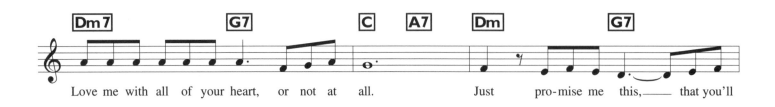

Love me with all of your heart, or not at all. Just pro-mise me this,— that you'll

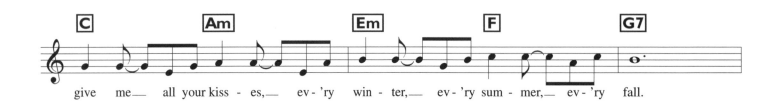

give me— all your kiss- es,— ev-'ry win- ter,— ev-'ry sum- mer,— ev-'ry fall.

When we are far a- part— or when you're near me,— love me with all of your heart as I love you.

Don't give me your love— for a mo - ment— or an hour,— love me al - ways— as you lov'd me— from the

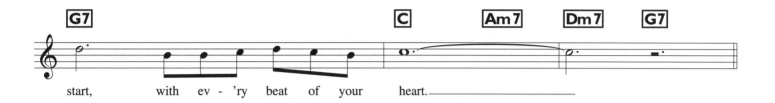

start, with ev - 'ry beat of your heart.___

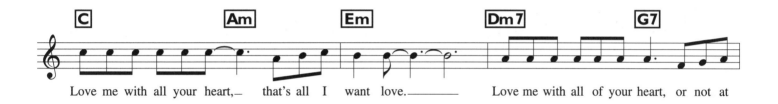

Love me with all your heart,— that's all I want love.___ Love me with all of your heart, or not at

all. Just pro - mise me this,___ that you'll give me— all your kiss - es,— ev - 'ry

win - ter,— ev - 'ry sum - mer,— ev - 'ry fall. When we are far a - part— or when you're near me,___

love me with all of your heart as I love you. Don't give me your love— for a mo - ment— or an hour,— love me

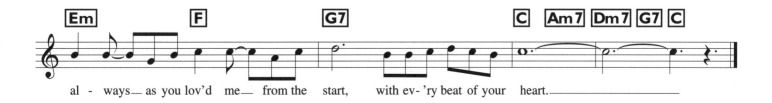

al - ways— as you lov'd me— from the start, with ev - 'ry beat of your heart.___

LOVIN' YOU

Words & Music by Minnie Riperton & Richard Rudolph

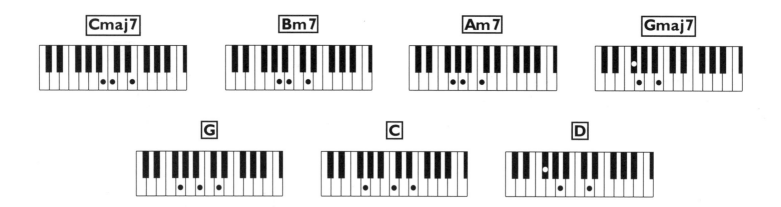

Voice: **Jazz Organ**

Rhythm: **16 Beat**

Tempo: ♩ = 66

Lov - in' you ___ is ea - sy 'cause you're beau - ti - ful, mak-ing love with you ___ is all ___

___ I wan - na do. ___ Lov - in' you is more than just ___ a dream come true, ___

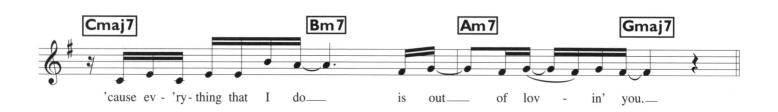

'cause ev - 'ry - thing that I do ___ is out ___ of lov - in' you.

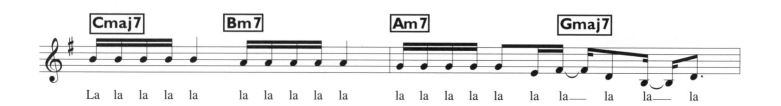

La la la la la la la la la la la la la la la la la ___ la la - la

doo doo dim doo doo.___ Ah._____

No - one else___ can make___ me feel___ the col - ors that___ you bring,___

stay with me___ while we___ grow old___ and we___ will live each day in spring-time;

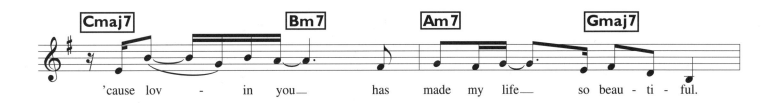

'cause lov - in you___ has made my life___ so beau - ti - ful.

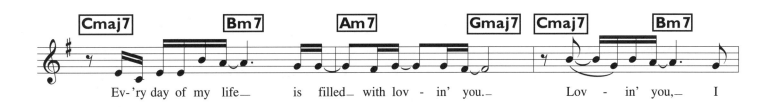

Ev-'ry day of my life___ is filled___ with lov - in' you.___ Lov - in' you,___ I

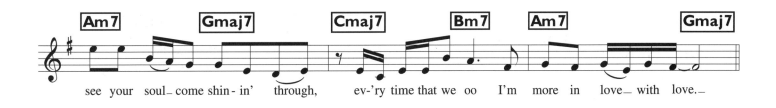

see your soul___ come shin - in' through, ev-'ry time that we oo I'm more in love___ with love.___

Repeat to fade

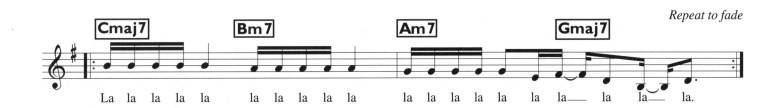

La la la la la la la la la la la la la la la la la___ la la___ la.

25

SOMETHIN' STUPID

Words & Music by C. Carson Parks

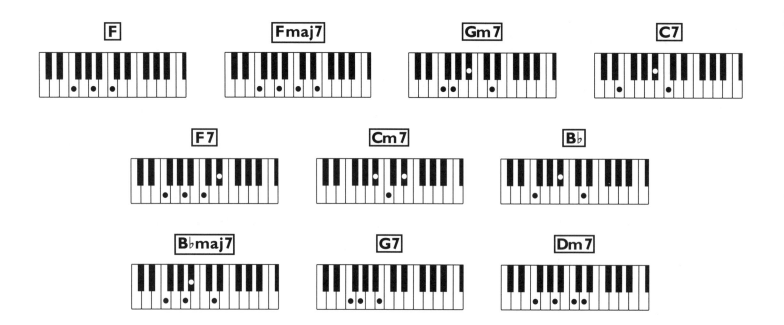

Voice: **Trumpet**

Rhythm: **16 Beat**

Tempo: ♩ = 92

I know I stand in line un-til you think you have the time to spend an eve-nin' with me.—

And if we go some place to dance, I know that there's a chance you won't be leav-in' with me.—

Then af-ter-wards we drop in-to a qui-et lit-tle place and have a drink or two.—

And then I go and spoil it all by say-in' some-thin' stu-pid like "I love you."

I can see it in your eyes that you de-spise the same old lines you heard the night be-fore.

And though it's just a line to you, for me it's true and ne-ver seemed so right be-fore.

I prac-tise ev-'ry day to find some cle-ver lines to say to make the mean-ing come through.

But then I think I'll wait un-til the eve-nin' gets late and I'm a-lone with you.

The time is right, your per-fume fills my head, the stars get red, and oh the night's so blue,

And then I go and spoil it all by say-in' some-thin' stu-pid like "I love you."

SUNNY

Words & Music by Bobby Hebb

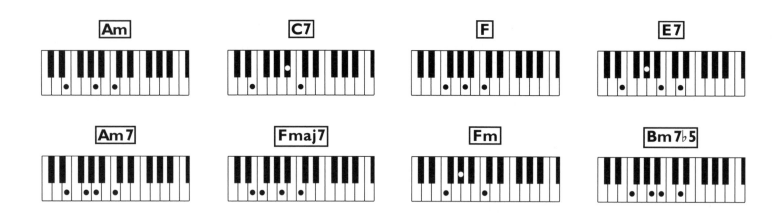

Voice: **Jazz Guitar**

Rhythm: **Rock**

Tempo: ♩ = 108

Sun - ny,_____ yes - ter - day my

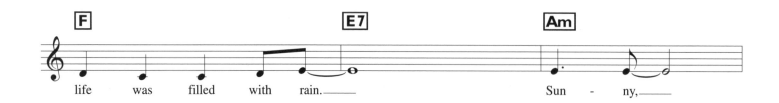

life was filled with rain._____ Sun - ny,_____

you smiled at me and real - ly eased the pain._____ Oh the

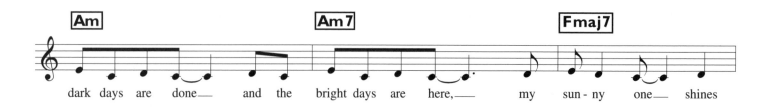

dark days are done___ and the bright days are here,_____ my sun - ny one___ shines

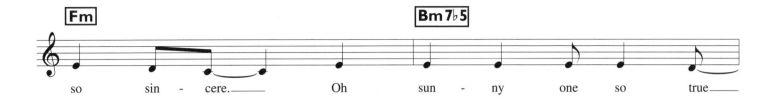

so sin - cere._____ Oh sun - ny one so true_____

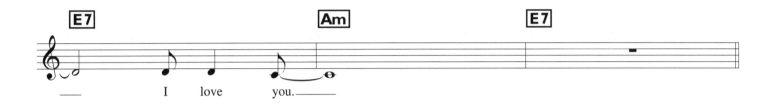

____ I love you._____

Sun - ny,____ thank - you for the truth you've let me see.___

____ Sun - ny,____ thank - you for the

facts from A to Z.____ My____ life____ was torn____ like____

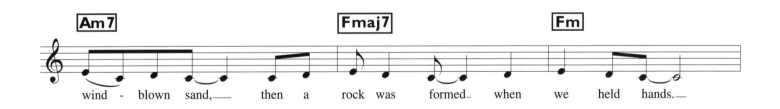

wind - blown sand,____ then a rock was formed_ when we held hands.____

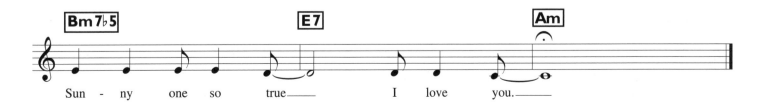

Sun - ny one so true_____ I love you._____

TAKE MY BREATH AWAY

Words by Tom Whitlock
Music by Giorgio Moroder

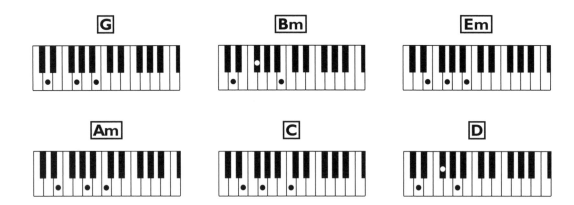

Voice: **Clarinet**

Rhythm: **Rock**

Tempo: ♩ = 96

Watch-in' ev-'ry mo-tion in___ my fool-ish lov-er's game;___

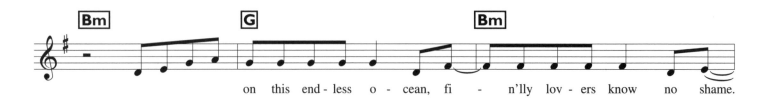

on this end-less o-cean, fi-n'lly lov-ers know no shame.

Turn - ing and re - turn - ing to

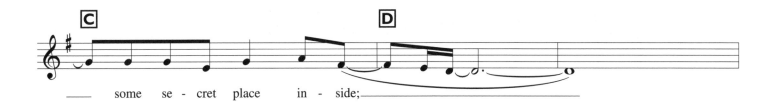

some se - cret place in - side;

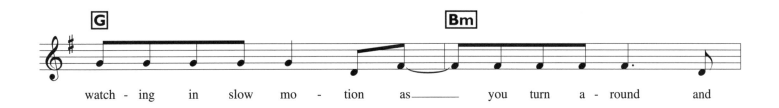

watch - ing in slow mo - tion as you turn a - round and

say, "Take my breath a - way."

My love, "Take my breath a -

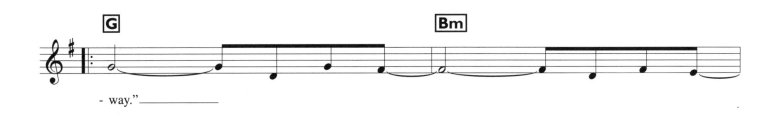

- way."

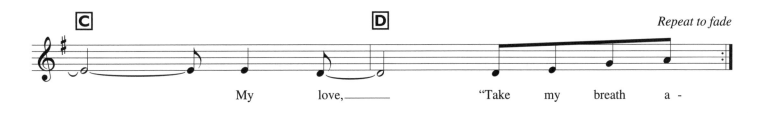

Repeat to fade

My love, "Take my breath a -

THE NEARNESS OF YOU

Music by Hoagy Carmichael
Words by Ned Washington

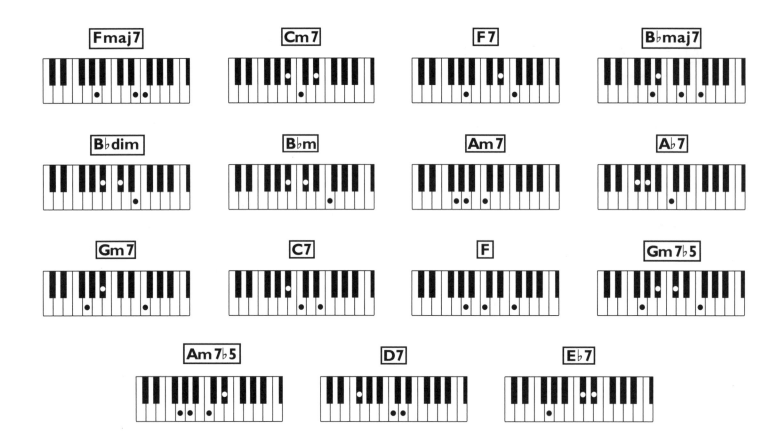

Voice: **Jazz Organ**

Rhythm: **Ballad**

Tempo: ♩ = 92

It's not the pale moon that ex - cites me, that thrills and de - lights me. Oh,

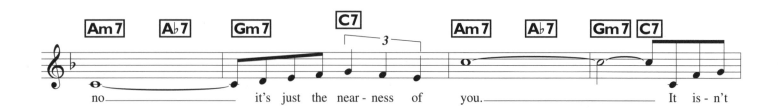

no_____ it's just the near - ness of you._____ It is - n't

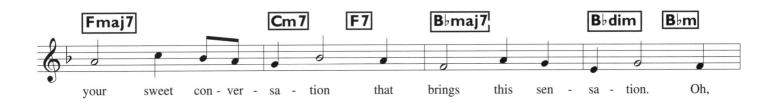

your sweet con - ver - sa - tion that brings this sen - sa - tion. Oh,

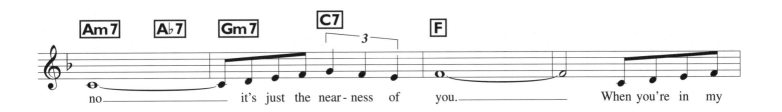

no_____ it's just the near - ness of you._____ When you're in my

arms_____ and I feel you so close to me,_____ all my

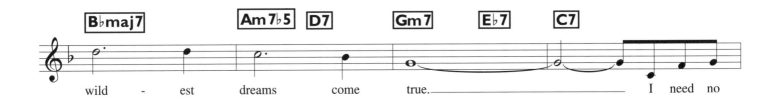

wild - est dreams come true._____ I need no

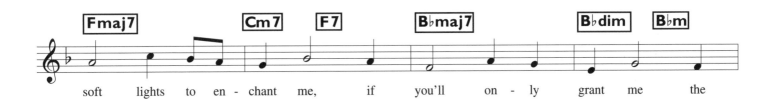

soft lights to en - chant me, if you'll on - ly grant me the

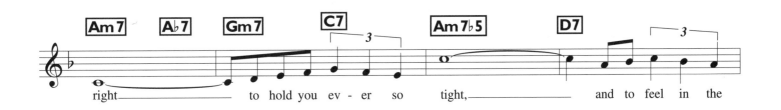

right_____ to hold you ev - er so tight,_____ and to feel in the

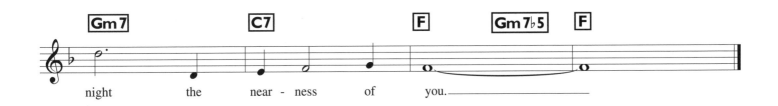

night the near - ness of you._____

THE TOUCH OF YOUR LIPS

Words & Music by Ray Noble

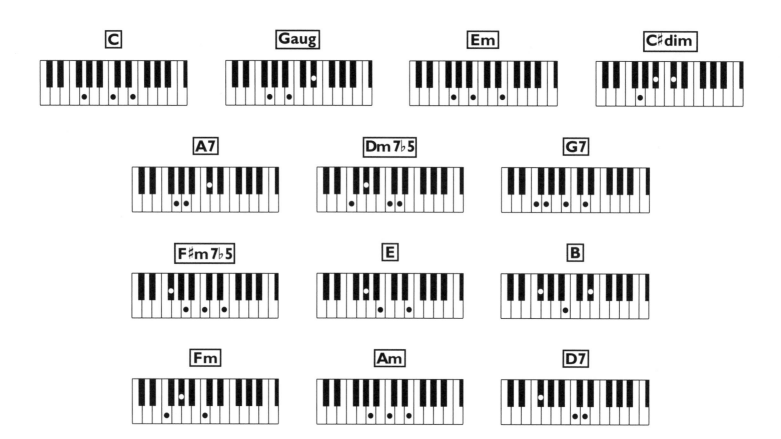

Voice: **Trumpet**

Rhythm: **Beguine**

Tempo: ♩ = 112

The touch of your lips____ up - on my brow;____ your

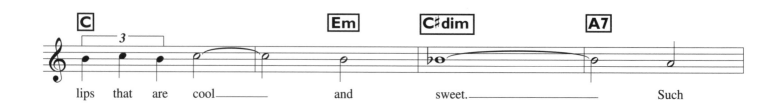

lips that are cool____ and sweet.____ Such

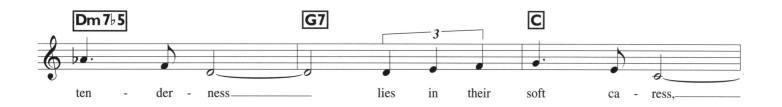

ten - der - ness_____ lies in their soft ca - ress,_____

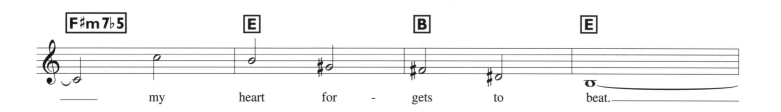

_____ my heart for - gets to beat._____

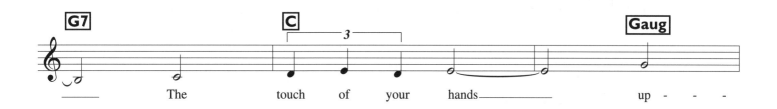

_____ The touch of your hands_____ up - - -

on my head,_____ the love in your eyes_____

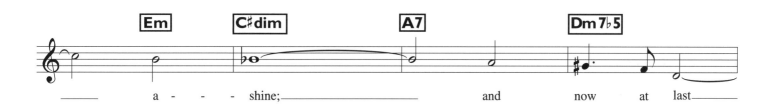

_____ a - - - shine;_____ and now at last_____

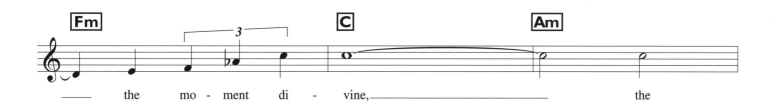

_____ the mo - ment di - vine,_____ the

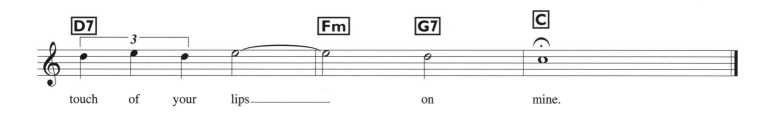

touch of your lips_____ on mine.

THE WAY YOU LOOK TONIGHT

Music by Jerome Kern
Words by Dorothy Fields

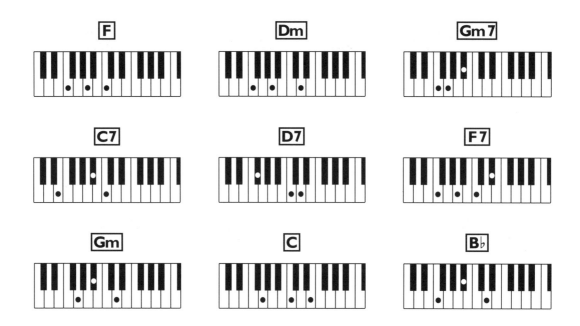

Voice: **Jazz Organ**

Rhythm: **16 Beat**

Tempo: ♩ = 120

Some   day   when I'm awf - 'ly

low,   when the world is cold,

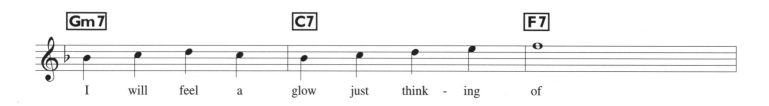

I will feel a   glow just think - ing of

you and the way you look to - -

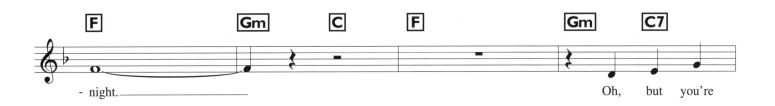

- night._____ Oh, but you're

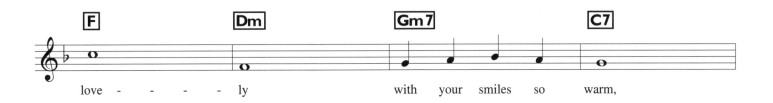

love - - - ly with your smiles so warm,

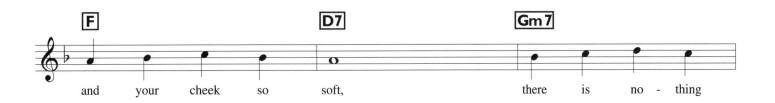

and your cheek so soft, there is no - thing

for me but to love you

just the way you look to - night.

Just the way you look to - - night._____

THE WIND BENEATH MY WINGS

Words & Music by Jeff Silbar & Larry Henley

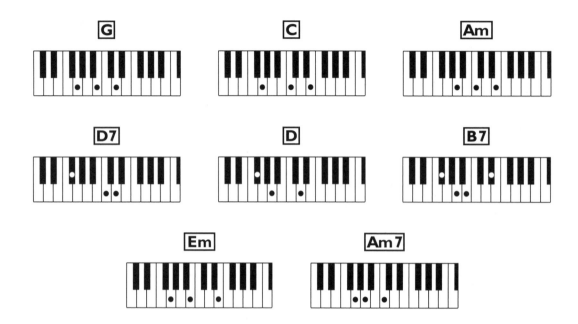

Voice: **Jazz Organ**

Rhythm: **16 beat**

Tempo: ♩ = 104

It must have been cold__ there__ in my sha - dow,

to ne - ver have sun - light__ on your face.

You've been con - tent__ to let me shine,

you al - ways walked___ the step be - hind.___

Did you ev - er know___ that you're my___ he - ro,

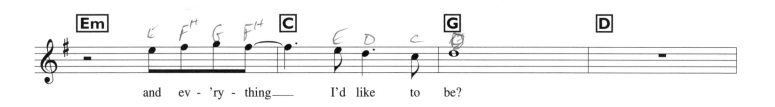

and ev - 'ry - thing___ I'd like to be?

I can fly high - - - er than an ea - - - - -

- gle,_____ 'cause you are the wind___ be - neath my

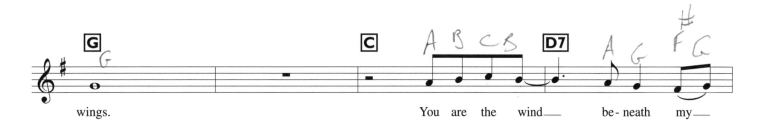

wings. You are the wind___ be - neath my___

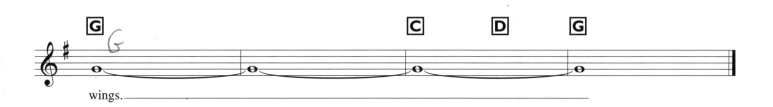

wings.___

TO EACH HIS OWN

Words & Music by Jay Livingston & Ray Evans

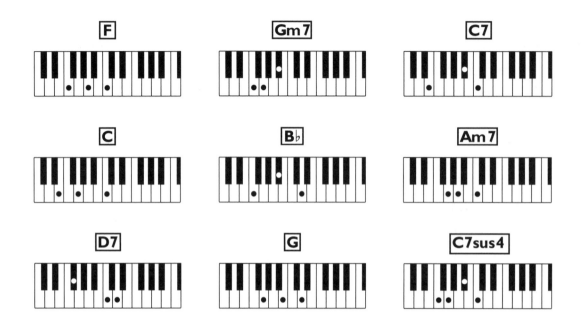

Voice: **Electric Organ**

Rhythm: **Foxtrot**

Tempo: ♩ = 96

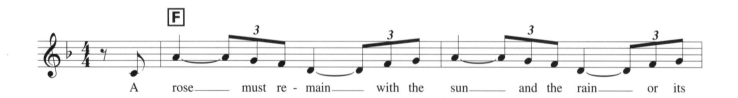

A rose_____ must re-main_____ with the sun_____ and the rain_____ or its

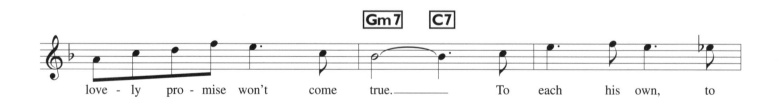

love-ly pro-mise won't come true._____ To each his own, to

each his own, and my own is you._____ What

good— is a song— if the words just don't be - long———— and a dream must be a dream for

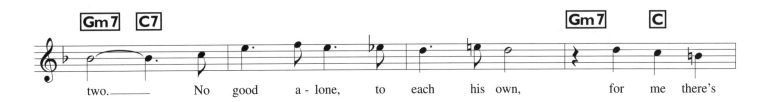

two.———— No good a - lone, to each his own, for me there's

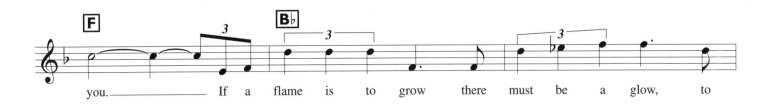

you.———— If a flame is to grow there must be a glow, to

o - pen the door there's a key.———— I need you to know, I can't let you go, your

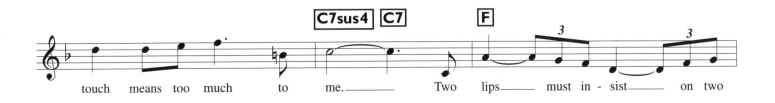

touch means too much to me.———— Two lips—— must in - sist—— on two

more——— to be kissed—— or they'll ne - ver know what love can do.———— To

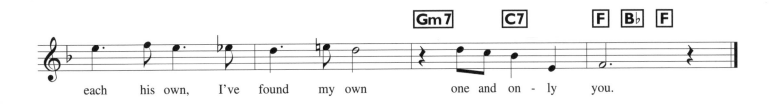

each his own, I've found my own one and on - ly you.

TRY A LITTLE TENDERNESS

Words & Music by Harry Woods, Jimmy Campbell & Reg Connelly

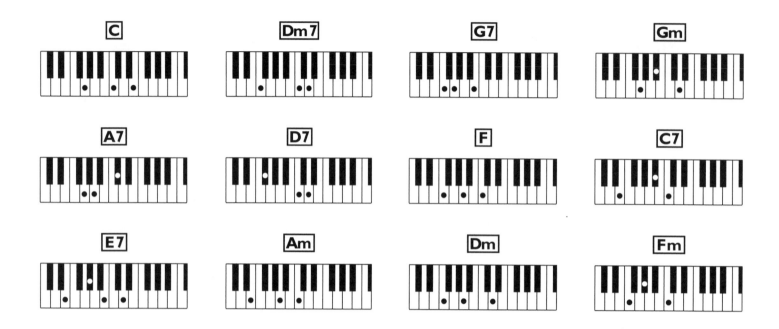

Voice: **Clarinet**

Rhythm: **16 beat**

Tempo: ♩ = 84

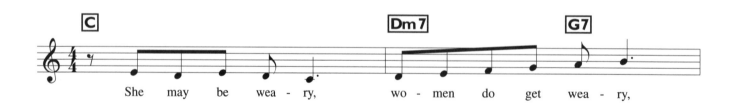

She may be wea - ry, wo - men do get wea - ry,

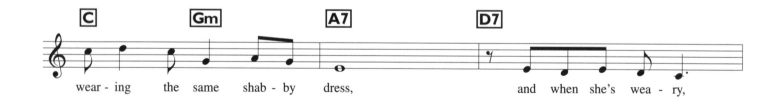

wear - ing the same shab - by dress, and when she's wea - ry,

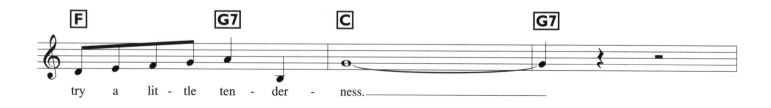

try a lit - tle ten - der - ness._____

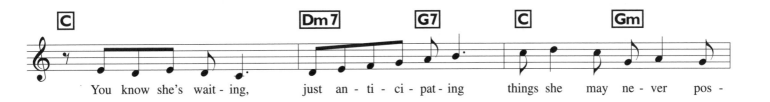

You know she's wait-ing, just an-ti-ci-pat-ing things she may ne-ver pos-

-sess. While she's with-out them try a lit-tle ten-der-

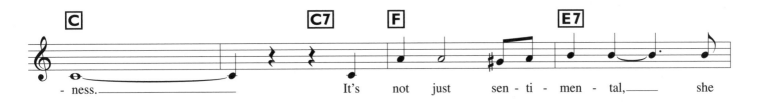

-ness. It's not just sen-ti-men-tal, she

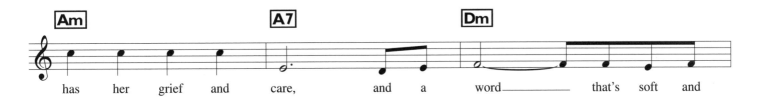

has her grief and care, and a word that's soft and

gen-tle makes it ea-si-er to bear. You won't re-gret it,

wo-men don't for-get it, love is their whole hap-pi-ness.

It's all so ea-sy, try a lit-tle ten-der-ness.

UP WHERE WE BELONG

Words & Music by Jack Nitzsche, Will Jennings & Buffy Sainte Marie

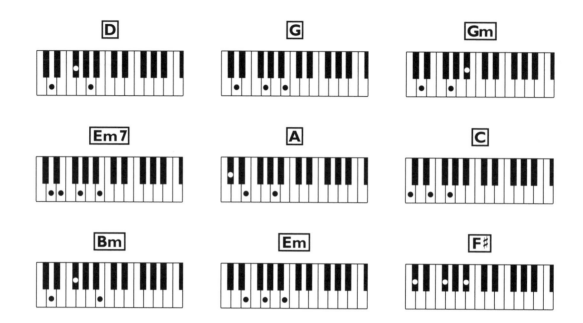

Voice: **Piano**

Rhythm: **16 Beat**

Tempo: ♩ = 84

Who knows what to - mor - row brings, — in a

world few hearts sur - vive? All I know is the

way I feel, — when it's real I keep it a - live. — The

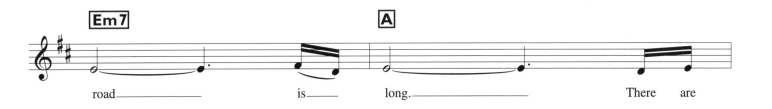

road_____ is____ long._____ There are

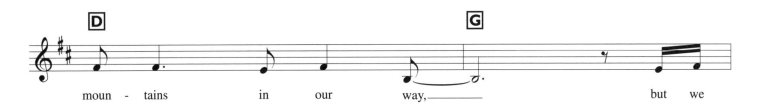

moun - tains in our way,____ but we

climb a step ev - 'ry day.

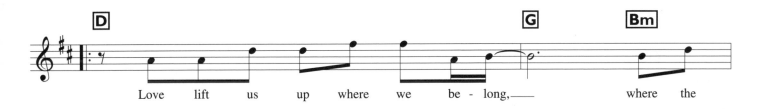

Love lift us up where we be - long,____ where the

ea - gles cry____ on a moun - tain high.

Love lift us up where we be - long,____ far from the

Repeat to fade

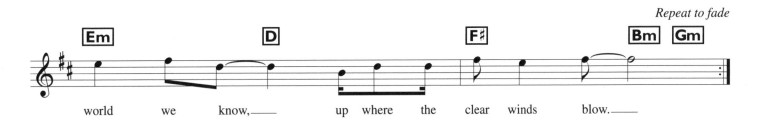

world we know,____ up where the clear winds blow.____

WHERE DO I BEGIN
(Theme from Love Story)

Music by Francis Lai
Words by Carl Sigman

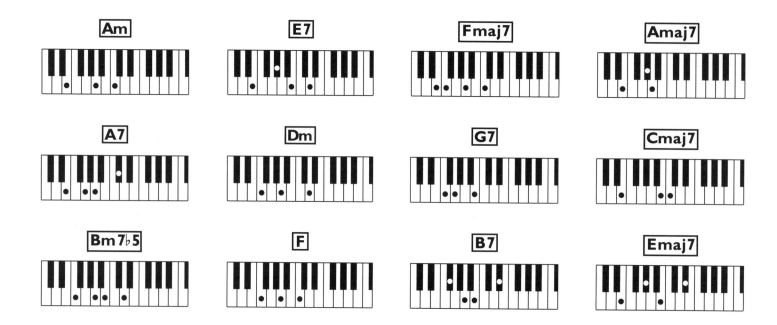

Voice: **Flute**

Rhythm: **Ballad**

Tempo: ♩ = 90

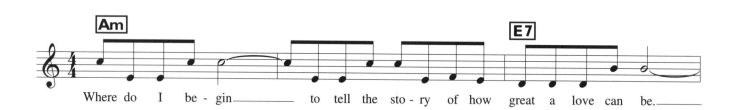

Where do I be - gin___ to tell the sto - ry of how great a love can be.___

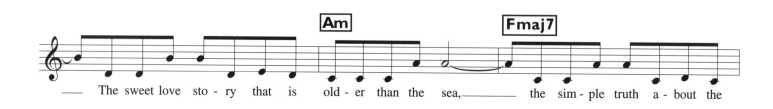

— The sweet love sto - ry that is old - er than the sea,_____ the sim - ple truth a - bout the

love she brings to me?_____ She fills my heart._____ She fills my

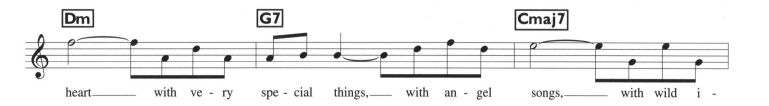

heart_____ with ve - ry spe - cial things,_____ with an - gel songs,_____ with wild i -

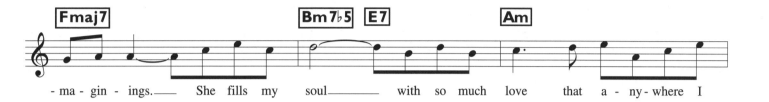

- ma - gin - ings._____ She fills my soul_____ with so much love that a - ny - where I

go_____ I'm ne - ver lone - ly._____ With her a - long_____ who could be

lone - ly?_____ I reach for her hand,_____ it's al - ways there._____

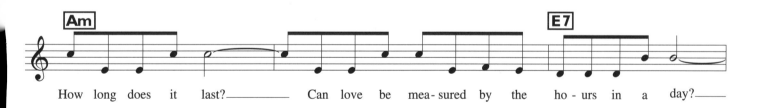

How long does it last?_____ Can love be mea - sured by the ho - urs in a day?_____

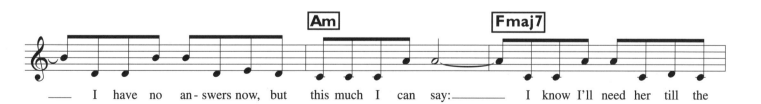

_____ I have no an - swers now, but this much I can say:_____ I know I'll need her till the

stars all burn a - way,_____ and she'll be there._____

EASIEST KEYBOARD COLLECTION

Easy-to-play melody line arrangements for all keyboards with chord symbols and lyrics. Suggested registration, rhythm and tempo are included for each song together with keyboard diagrams showing left-hand chord voicings used.

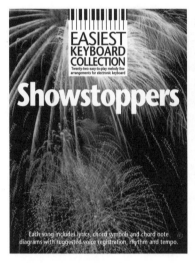

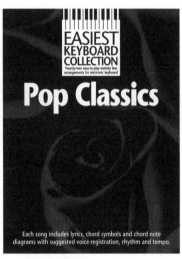

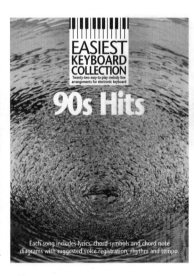

Showstoppers

Consider Yourself (Oliver!), Do You Hear The People Sing? (Les Misérables), I Know Him So Well (Chess), Maria (West Side Story), Smoke Gets In Your Eyes (Roberta) and 17 more big stage hits.
Order No. AM944218

Pop Classics

A Whiter Shade Of Pale (Procol Harum), Bridge Over Troubled Water (Simon & Garfunkel), Crocodile Rock (Elton John) and nineteen more classic pop hits, including Hey Jude (The Beatles), Imagine (John Lennon), Massachusetts (The Bee Gees) and Stars (Simply Red).
Order No. AM944196

90s Hits

Over twenty of the greatest hits of the 1990s, including Always (Bon Jovi), Fields Of Gold (Sting), Have I Told You Lately (Rod Stewart), One Sweet Day (Mariah Carey), Say You'll Be There (Spice Girls), and Wonderwall (Oasis).
Order No. AM944229

TV Themes

Twenty-two great themes from popular TV series, including Casualty, EastEnders, Gladiators, Heartbeat, I'm Always Here (Baywatch), Red Dwarf and The Black Adder.
Order No. AM944207

Also available...

Film Themes, Order No. AM952050   **Chart Hits**, Order No. AM952083

Jazz Classics, Order No. AM952061   **Classical Themes**, Order No. AM952094

Classic Blues, Order No. AM950697   **Christmas**, Order No. AM952105

Love Songs, Order No. AM950708   **Ballads**, Order No. AM952116

Pop Hits, Order No. AM952072   **Broadway**, Order No. AM952127